S.P.I.R.E.®

2nd Edition

Reader Level 3

Sheila Clark-Edmands

EDUCATORS PUBLISHING SERVICE
Cambridge and Toronto

Acquisitions/Development: Bonnie Lass
Senior editor: Jen Noon
Acquisitions assistant: Eryn Kline
Managing editor: Sheila Neylon
Cover illustration: Ruth Linstromberg
Cover design: Karen Lomigora
Typesetting: Debbie Sidman

Printed in Hartland, WI, in February 2011
ISBN 978-0-8388-2708-6

9 10 11 CCI 14 13 12 11

Contents

he	no	by
she	go	my
we	so	try
me	also	fly
be		spy
belong		spry
before		why
begin		pry

New Sight Word

gone

Review Sight Words

the, has, is, a, his, I, was, to, do, said, what, you, who, into, of, full, pull, push, put, through, your, walk, talk, want, live, give, have, one, done, some, come, something, someone, where, there, were, are, somewhere, love

quack	tick	shot	shed	sing
time	slide	pants	when	lunch
fly	white	black	pry	pond
pitch	tent	she	Jack	then
mess	go	class	check	stung

She will try to come back.

Do you want to fly the plane?

Can you go to the game?

He will fry the fish in the pan.

Why did you come late to class?

Can you pry the lid off the can?

Is the milk all gone?

We can all go to the game.

I will dry the wet cloth on the line.

Do not cry.

so, he, fly, review *V-e, tch, ck, qu, wa, al, ff, ll, ss,*
nk, ng, wh, th, ch, sh, short vowels
Decoding/Sentence Reading 1

Late

The bell rang. Jane was late. She ran to math class. Miss Frank did not smile.

"I will try to tell you why I am late," said Jane.

"No, thanks," said Miss Frank. "This is the sixth time you are late. So you will go home and get your dad to send me a note."

Jane left math class. She felt sad.

When she got home, Dad was upset. He said, "You cannot go to the big game, Jane. You will have to miss it."

"Why did I have to be late? I will try to think next time," said Jane.

"Yes, you will," said Dad. "You will have a lot of time to think."

so, he, fly, review *V-e, tch, ck, qu, wa, al, ff, ll, ss, nk, ng, wh, th, ch, sh,* short vowels
Late

sent	best	fresh	name	slime
thing	split	crab	splash	ring
made	hole	slope	brag	shop
drift	grass	left	help	shed
snake	mule	pine	logs	flash

We will swim in the pond.

Try your best!

My snake is lost in the grass.

Can you be here at ten?

Can you go with me?

I want to talk to you before you go.

"I Spy" is a fun game.

Tim has <u>gone</u> to bed.

We will be best pals.

She has a cute dog!

so, he, fly, review V-e, tch, ck, qu, wa, al, ff, ll, ss, nk, ng, wh, th, ch, sh, short vowels

Decoding/Sentence Reading 2

The Big Catch

In the spring, Jake likes to fish at the pond. One spring, he went with his best pal, Fred, to fish.

Fred said, "We must try to catch a big bass! My mom will fry it when we get home."

"Yes, let's try," said Jake.

Jake put the skiff into the pond. Then he and Fred got into it and went to the best spot to fish. Jake had lots of grubs that he had dug up. Fred held the pan of grubs. Jake held his rod. He put one grub on the end of his line.

Jake and Fred sat and sat.

"We have sat still a long time," said Fred. "Why? Where are the fish?"

"We want to go home with a big fish," said Jake. "Sit still, and try some more. The fish will come."

A fly sat on Fred's hat.

"What a big fly!" said Jake. "Let me get it!" Jake hit Fred's hat with his rod. The rod made Fred's hat fall into the pond.

"No! I must get it," said Fred. He got his hand on the hat, but it was stuck to Jake's line. The line was stuck in the pond. So, the hat was stuck on the line, and the line was stuck in the pond!

"Help me!" said Fred. "The hat is stuck, and the line is stuck. And I think I did catch a fish!"

Something big held on to the line, but Fred and Jake were strong. A fish came up on the end of the line. So did Fred's hat!

"Yikes!" said Jake. "That is a big fish. It is a big bass!" The fish made a big splash. Fred got hold of the bass and put it in the skiff.

"What a catch," said Fred.

"What a hat," said Jake.

so, he, fly, review *V-e, tch, ck, qu, wa, al, ff, ll, ss, nk, ng, wh, th, ch, sh,* short vowels

The Big Catch

more	shake	moth	here	snap
plan	wore	black	toss	smile
wire	patch	snack	that	when
bank	chick	swell	shine	quote
bunch	thanks	dress	left	blush

I left my snack at home.

Did you begin the job?

The chick ate a black fly.

I will try my best.

I can go to the store.

Why did you do that?

Did you cry when you fell?

Where can Kate be?

Where has she <u>gone</u>?

Jack lost the strap on his bag.

A Camp in the Hills

I will tell you of a time when Dad and I went to camp and fish. We went up Flat Rock Hill. It was a long hike. At last, we came to a spot to pitch the tent. It was beside a lake. We cut a big branch to prop up the tent. The tent was up in no time at all. Then we went to the lake to fish.

Dad and I got in the skiff with the rods. We sat in the skiff on the lake. Dad got five rock bass. I had no luck. We went back to the camp, and I made a campfire all by myself.

"I will fry up the fish," said Dad.

He did a fine job. I ate more than at home. We went to bed. We slept well by the fire, and at six, we woke up. The sun was up, and a mist was still on the lake.

Dad and I got up, ate something, and went on a long hike. We like to hike.

so, he, fly, review *V-e, tch, ck, qu, wa, al, ff, ll, ss, nk, ng, wh, th, ch, sh*, short vowels
A Camp in the Hills

We went up a tall hill. At the top of the hill was a big rock. I sat on the rock. Next to the rock was a thin snake. Did I jump! I got off the rock fast and ran to Dad.

"It is just a grass snake," Dad said to me. "It will not bite or strike at you."

I still did not want to sit next to a snake. So we went back to camp. Then we had to pack up and go home.

And that is the end of the tale of my trip.

so, he, fly, review *V-e, tch, ck, qu, wa, al, ff, ll, ss, nk, ng, wh, th, ch, sh,* short vowels

A Camp in the Hills

thick	vine	class	sink	got
swing	fetch	punch	small	then
white	while	fed	that	tall
wash	batch	bake	shade	bride
save	wings	side	spend	plant

We can fly in the sky in a plane.

Can you sit beside me?

Dad will bake my cake.

Can you fetch me that small glass?

I will spend all my time in the shade.

I cannot cut this thick vine.

That tall man came to class.

Mom fed the tot while Dad got him some milk.

It is not fun to be late.

I swung on my swing until the sun was <u>gone</u>.

so, he, fly, review *V-e, tch, ck, qu, wa, al, ff, ll, ss,*
nk, ng, wh, th, ch, sh, **short vowels**
Decoding/Sentence Reading 4

Come Fly with Me

I can fly.

Will you try?

We can fly to the sky.

My, my, my.

Why can we fly to the sky?

We can fly with these wings.

Such fine things!

You can fly by my side.

The sky is so big and wide.

Up, up, up to the sky.

Come on! Watch me fly, fly, fly!

so, he, fly, review *V-e, tch, ck, qu, wa, al, ff, ll, ss, nk, ng, wh, th, ch, sh,* short vowels
Come Fly With Me

Exceptions: *-ild*, *-ind*, *-old*, *-ost*, *-oll*

child	bind	old	most	toll
wild	blind	bold	post	stroll
mild	find	cold	host	troll
	kind	gold	almost	roll
	hind	hold		droll
	mind	mold		scroll
	wind	sold		
	grind	told		
	rind	scold		

New Sight Words

both, climb, clothes

Review Sight Words

the, has, is, a, his, I, was, to, do, said, what, you, who,
into, of, full, pull, push, put, through, your, walk, talk,
want, live, give, have, one, done, some, come, something,
someone, where, there, were, are, somewhere, love, gone

snake	risk	cold	dog	soft
smack	ball	thank	think	tall
smell	grim	drape	most	state
child	stone	batch	quick	drive
fresh	stamp	trip	sack	best

The old man took a stroll.

The child sat in the crib.

The pond water was cold.

The old king has a chest full of gold.

Can you hold this stone?

This wild cat is bold.

Did you find my gold watch?

I cannot find where it has gone.

I told you to get the dog.

The child was kind to me.

exceptions, review *so, he, fly, V-e, tch, ck, qu, wa, al,*
ff, ll, ss, nk, ng, wh, th, ch, sh, short vowels
Decoding/Sentence Reading 1

13

Old Pals

Jed was just a child, but he was kind. He was kind to his mom and dad. He was kind to pets. And he was kind to his pals, like Mr. Gold. Mr. Gold was an old man at the end of the block who Jed did talk to and check up on.

One time, Mr. Gold gave Jed some cash and a list to take to the store. Jed did not mind the hike to the store. It was a fine walk. At the store, he had to ask Miss Post to help him find the rolls and the eggs.

When Jed got back, Mr. Gold made him lunch. Then Jed and Mr. Gold had a chat. Jed and Mr. Gold <u>both</u> told some old jokes.

Then Mr. Gold said, "You are a kind child. I am so glad you are my pal."

"You are a kind man," said Jed. "You make me lunch and tell me jokes. We have fun."

This made Mr. Gold smile. "We are old pals," he said. "Well, one of us is old. One of us is still a child."

This made Jed grin. "Then we are just pals," he said.

exceptions, review *so, he, fly, V-e, tch, ck, qu, wa, al, ff, ll, ss, nk, ng, wh, th, ch, sh,* short vowels
Old Pals

note	gift	fine	hive	next
skip	plot	step	truck	grin
trust	soft	swim	note	stop
nine	gold	most	use	cave
black	find	end	smile	smell
snore	lost	last	shop	host

Calvin did not mind the cold.

Wind the top, and it will spin.

James had a gold ring.

The child dug in the soft sand.

The old dog was blind.

It is bold to jump from a plane.

Jill had a bad cold, so she did not go with Ron.

Eve sold the gold watch.

My dad is the best host.

Jan ate the lime rind.

exceptions, review *so, he, fly, V-e, tch, ck, qu, wa, al, ff, ll, ss, nk, ng, wh, th, ch, sh*, short vowels

Decoding/Sentence Reading 2

The Ring

Ted was in a bind. He had to get a gift, and he was in a rush. He ran into a store.

"Do you still have that brass ring?" said Ted.

"No, we sold it," said the man in the store.

"I want a gift to give to my best pal, Cass," said Ted.

"We have gold rings," said the man. "This one is on sale."

This made Ted smile. "It is the most I have spent on a gift, but Cass will like it. I have to get more cash. Can you hold the ring while I go to the bank?"

"Yes," said the man. "But you must not be late. The store will close at five."

Ted ran to the bank, got the cash, and went back to the store. It was almost five. He had the man put the ring in a black box with a gold lid.

Ted gave the ring to Cass.

"Ted! I like it so much!" said Cass. She put on the ring and held up the hand. "I have an old brass ring that I do not like that much. But gold is the best! I will not take this ring off."

"What luck!" Ted said to himself. "I am glad that the brass ring was sold and I had to get the gold one!"

exceptions, review *so, he, fly, V-e, tch, ck, qu, wa, al,*
ff, ll, ss, nk, ng, wh, th, ch, sh, short vowels
The Ring

ditch	melt	felt	send	chick
joke	make	brave	clap	flash
risk	spend	sniff	bite	nine
let	bath	pipe	hunt	rest
jump	west	sell	such	blame

I do not mind if you sit on the bench.

The bold pup can stand on his hind legs.

If you close the gate with a slam, it will scare the old dog.

You can hold the chick in your hand.

Rose sold almost all her old <u>clothes</u> at the junk sale.

I want to help the child find his mom.

The flat ball cannot roll.

The blind child can do most things by himself.

Did you find my dime?

My dime fell into this ditch.

exceptions, review *so, he, fly, V-e, tch, ck, qu, wa, al,*
ff, ll, ss, nk, ng, wh, th, ch, sh, short vowels
Decoding and Sentence Reading 3

I Love That Child of Mine

He can be wild,
But I love my child.
He is quite bold,
And can't be told
What to do.

I can try,
But he is sly.
I do not mind.
He is so kind.
What can you do?

My child is cute.
He is no brute.
If he is sad,
I make him glad.
It's what moms do—

Help you, hug you,
Hold you, love you!

exceptions, review *so, he, fly, V-e, tch, ck, qu, wa, al,*
ff, ll, ss, nk, ng, wh, th, ch, sh, short vowels
I Love That Child of Mine

19

crust	brim	crab	dusk	tore
more	lake	spade	belt	bunch
camp	post	ditch	rust	state
nine	vote	help	size	hope
and	shut	king	catch	path

I told Lin to pick up the <u>clothes</u>.

<u>Both</u> of you can help dig the ditch.

Do not jump into the cold lake.

The vest has a gold pin on the back.

Can you help me <u>climb</u> to the top?

I told you to help Clare.

Jeff sold the last cake in the shop.

It is brave to be bold.

The old plug gave Dad a mild shock.

The lamp almost fell off the lamppost.

The Bold Robins

It is spring. The robin sings as she makes a nest of twigs, mud, and grass. The nest has a cup shape. When the robin has eggs, she will put them all in this nest. Then she will sit on the eggs a long time.

The eggs hatch and the hatchlings want to be fed. A hatchling is a small robin. Robins like an insect for lunch and love to munch on a plump fly.

The mom robin gets bugs and pulls things from the grass to give to the small hatchlings. The hatchlings are fed by the mom robin. The bugs go from the mom's bill to the hatchlings' bills.

The hatchlings get big, almost as big as the mom robin! They become small robins. And they get bold and brave! So the bold, brave robins try to fly, and the bold, brave robins fall. But the robins try and try. At last the robins can fly up into the sky. The robins are gone and the mom is left behind. She is sad that the robins have gone, but she is glad that the robins will do well in life.

exceptions, review *so, he, fly, V-e, tch, ck, qu, wa, al,*
ff, ll, ss, nk, ng, wh, th, ch, sh, short vowels
The Bold Robins

21

play	hay	may	stay	spray
way	stray	say	pay	day
jay	bay	ray	gray	tray
fray	sway	clay	bray	lay
playtime	haystack	playmate	subway	pray
				Sunday

New Sight Words

they, says, today

Review Sight Words

the, has, is, a, his, I, was, to, do, said, what, you, who, into, of, full, pull, push, put, through, your, walk, talk, want, live, give, have, one, done, some, come, something, someone, where, there, were, are, somewhere, love, gone, both, climb, clothes

say	ash	state	lay	note
not	lunch	stay	home	scrap
skin	glide	gray	pay	skill
play	take	spin	spend	plate
day	went	hatch	risk	clay

Sunday is the best day.

This is a fun game to play.

I like to ride the subway.

Ray will take Liz to the play.

I like to stay inside on a hot day.

Did you pay the man in the store?

The gray cat lay on the bed.

The day went by fast.

The hen will lay an egg.

Jay is one of my playmates.

The Subway Ride

Kay likes to ride the subway, but not Clare. She hates it. When <u>they</u> go to Gram's, Kay and Clare must take the subway. <u>They</u> both love to be with Gram, so <u>they</u> want to go.

"This will be a fun day," said Kay. "I love to ride the subway!"

"Maybe you do," said Clare. "But subway rides scare some of us!"

"Just stay by my side," said Kay. "I have a map."

"I hope we do not get lost," said Clare. "There are all those stops. When will we get off?"

"I will tell you. I have the subway map," said Kay. "Clare, here is the subway line we want. Get on and stay close to me."

-ay, review exceptions, *so, he, fly, V-e, tch, ck, qu, wa, al, ff, ll, ss, nk, ng, wh, th, ch, sh,* short vowels

The Subway Ride

Kay and Clare got on. <u>They</u> sat side by side. As the subway sped up, the map fell. It sat there. Clare had to pick it up. "Kay!" she said. "We have to have this map! Do you want to stay on the subway all day long?"

"Maybe," said Kay. "I love to ride the subway. I told you that."

"Well, I hate it," said Clare. "So <u>today</u> I will hold the map."

Kay had to smile. "You do that," she said as the subway came to a stop. "Is this the stop we want? You have to say, Clare. You have the map."

With a yell, Clare gave the map back to Kay. Six stops went by. Then Kay said to get off. She was sad to get off the subway. But Clare was quite glad!

-ay, review exceptions, *so, he, fly, V-e, tch, ck, qu, wa, al,*
ff, ll, ss, nk, ng, wh, th, ch, sh, short vowels
The Subway Ride

25

chess	playmate	bug	top	Hank
tray	think	wish	yell	sway
swing	sun	bring	moth	may
hall	bench	itch	camp	Sunday
drive	hallway	bay	stone	Jay

Dad <u>says</u> that you may stay and play.

The welt on Tim's leg stung.

Jade dug in the soft sand.

You were gone a long time.

The ball hit Jay in the chest.

Pay the man in the gray vest.

Can you find your way home?

Gale told Tom that she did not want to go to the store.

Jay sold his best gold ring last Sunday.

May we play by the bay?

-ay, review exceptions, *so, he, fly, V-e, tch, ck, qu, wa, al, ff, ll, ss, nk, ng, wh, th, ch, sh*, short vowels

Decoding/Sentence Reading 2

The Gray Day

When Max got up, he was glad. He had made a plan with his pal Jay. "Jay and I will go to the lake at one. <u>Today</u> will be a fun day!" said Max.

At nine, Max went to check the sky. It was gray. Max went in and said to his mom, "The sky is gray. I want the sun to shine so it will get hot. Jay and I want to swim in the lake at one. I don't want this to be a gray day."

"The forecast <u>says</u> there will be some sun by one," said Mom. "Do something to pass the time till then."

"Do something? Like what?" said Max.

"You can play with your clay," said Mom. "Make a clay pot."

"No. I have made lots of pots," said Max.

"You can put this dish and cup on the tray and take them to the sink," said Mom.

"That will not take long," said Max. "May I wash them? That will take some time."

-ay, review exceptions, *so, he, fly, V-e, tch, ck, qu, wa, al, ff, ll, ss, nk, ng, wh, th, ch, sh*, short vowels
The Gray Day

Mom had to smile. "Here is what you can do to pass the time, Max. You can do some chores and I will pay you. You can use the cash at the lake."

"Way to go!" said Max with a grin. "I can get a snack at the lake!"

So Max did some chores, and the day *did* go by fast.

When Max and Jay met at the lake at one, there was a ray of sun in the sky. "I have cash!" said Max. "We can share a snack."

"Thanks, Max," said Jay. "I just hope the sun will stay the rest of the day!"

And it did. It was a fine day at last.

-ay, review exceptions, so, he, fly, V-e, tch, ck, qu, wa, al,
ff, ll, ss, nk, ng, wh, th, ch, sh, short vowels
The Gray Day

past	play	must	help	fish
sank	long	hay	run	bass
say	Sunday	this	when	call
lunch	clay	hole	pick	rope
child	gray	stay	jay	day

The sun's rays can be hot.

Can you come this Sunday?

What a hot day!

Can you stay and have lunch?

It was a mild spring day when Tam left to go fish at the pond.

You must not play all day!

A child likes to play.

Can you punch a hole in the clay?

When will your mom pick you up?

We will have ham at lunch on Sunday.

The Best Day

It was Sunday. Tess did not want to go to Gram's with Mom and Dad. "What can I do there? Who can I play with?" she said. "I want to stay home."

"No, Tess," said Mom. "You have to come. Gram loves you, and you love Gram."

"Yes, I do," said Tess. "Well, I will come, but this will not be a fun day."

Mom, Dad, and Tess drove to Gram's. When <u>they</u> got there, Tess ran to hug and kiss Gram.

"Tess, go play in the hayloft while we make lunch," said Gram.

"By myself?" said Tess. "That's not much fun."

Gram had to smile, but she just said, "Go to the hayloft. Trust me. You will have fun. Someone is there who you will like. She is in the same grade as you."

-ay, review exceptions, *so, he, fly, V-e, tch, ck, qu, wa, al, ff, ll, ss, nk, ng, wh, th, ch, sh,* short vowels
The Best Day

Tess ran to the hayloft. Someone was up there. Someone said, "My name is Jan. My home is next to your Gram's. You must be Tess."

"Yes, I am," said Tess. "Do you want to play with me?"

"Yes!" said Jan. "Climb up."

The climb was fast. When Tess got up to the top of the hayloft, Jan said, "We can slide on the side of the haystack. Will you give me a push when I get to the top of the hay?"

Jan gave a Tess a push, and Tess slid. Next Tess went to the top of the hay, and Jan gave her a push. Jan slid on the side of the haystack. Then Jan ran to get something. It was a small, gray cat. "This is Clay," she said. "He was a stray cat who came to our home. I fed him and gave him a name. I love him a lot."

"He is so soft," said Tess, as she gave him a pat. "Clay is gray. Is that why you gave him the name Clay?"

"Yes, it is," said Jan with a grin.

-ay, review exceptions, *so, he, fly, V-e, tch, ck, qu, wa, al, ff, ll, ss, nk, ng, wh, th, ch, sh,* short vowels

The Best Day

Just then, Gram said to come in to have lunch. <u>They</u> all ate lunch. When it was time to go, Tess gave Jan a hug. "I had fun, Jan. You are a fine playmate!" she said.

"You are a pal!" said Jan. "We can play the next time you come here."

On the way home, Tess said, "I am so glad I did not stay home. I had the best time!"

-ay, review exceptions, *so, he, fly, V-e, tch, ck, qu, wa, al,*
ff, ll, ss, nk, ng, wh, th, ch, sh, short vowels
The Best Day

told	go	day	quiz	back
playmate	vine	lick	mule	cure
mole	lay	hutch	chop	walk
ray	when	stay	with	six
set	pill	hay	way	subway

The subway is a fast ride.

Can you stay a long time today?

My pal May is a fine playmate.

We will stand to sing this song.

Lay the gift on the bed.

It is fun to jump off the haystack.

I wash my hands before I have lunch.

The plate is on the top shelf of the hutch.

Dad says that this is the way home.

The mole dug a hole all the way up to the grass.

-ay, **review exceptions**, *so, he, fly, V-e, tch, ck, qu, wa, al,*
ff, ll, ss, nk, ng, wh, th, ch, sh, **short vowels**
Decoding/Sentence Reading 4

The Rays of the Sun

The sun helps you. You have to have the sun to live. The sun gives us day, so it is not black all the time. The sun makes it hot, so where we live is not as cold as can be all the time.

But the sun can also be bad. The sun's rays can do bad things to your skin. If it is a hot, hot, hot day with a lot of sun, stay in the shade when you can. Put on clothes that hide your skin. Put on sunblock. Put on a hat.

So watch when the sun shines on a hot day! Do not let a lot of sun get to your skin. That way, you will stay safe. Then you can have fun in the sun!

-ay, review exceptions, *so, he, fly, V-e, tch, ck, qu, wa, al, ff, ll, ss, nk, ng, wh, th, ch, sh*, short vowels
The Rays of the Sun

-ed (melted)

land	landed		
melt	melted		
hunt	hunted		
sift	sifted		
act	acted		
nest	nested		
last	lasted		
test	tested		
hand	handed		
print	printed		

-ed (smelled)

play	played
smell	smelled
stay	stayed
spell	spelled
pray	prayed
sway	swayed
yell	yelled
spray	sprayed
fill	filled
sway	swayed

-ed (winked)

rush	rushed	thank	thanked
crush	crushed	wink	winked
rock	rocked	stamp	stamped
jump	jumped	yank	yanked
pinch	pinched	ask	asked

Review Sight Words

the, has, is, a, his, I, was, to, do, said, what, you, who, into, of, full, pull, push, put, through, your, walk, talk, want, live, give, have, one, done, some, come, something, someone, where, there, were, are, somewhere, love, gone, both, climb, clothes, they, says, today

melted	played	trip	slam	filled
hole	punched	talk	talked	nested
when	this	yelled	lip	thing
hunted	well	toss	tossed	shop
stuck	rocked	pitch	asked	sifted

Flo sifted the sand and filled a bucket.

Ed played all day with his pals.

The man hunted and hunted to find his lost wallet.

Luke printed his name on the line.

Have you asked your mom if you can go?

Give the rope a tug.

Here is a bone to give the dog.

He ate the cake from a plate.

Jan tossed the ball to Ming.

Mom rocked the tot and put him to bed.

-ed, **review** *-ay*, **exceptions**, *so, he, fly, V-e, tch, ck, qu, wa, al,*
ff, ll, ss, nk, ng, wh, th, ch, sh, **short vowels**
Decoding/Sentence Reading 1

No Rest

Kit got on the plane. She wanted to rest on the way home. But she had no luck and got no rest! Here is why.

A child sat next to Kit on the plane. He played and acted like a brat. He bumped Kit with his small red truck. He pinched Kit's leg. His mom did not stop him at all, and this upset Kit quite a lot. At last the plane landed. It was on time. Kit was glad and rushed off the plane.

A man in a red cap met the plane. He told Kit where to pick up the bags. Kit ran to the spot. She lifted the bag off the bag belt and went to catch the bus.

When she got into the bus, she was shocked. There was the same child and his mom. The child yelled at Kit. His mom gave Kit a big smile. Kit did not smile back at them. She felt sick.

It was a long, long, long bus ride to Kit's home!

-ed, review -ay, exceptions, so, he, fly, V-e, tch, ck, qu, wa, al, ff, ll, ss, nk, ng, wh, th, ch, sh, short vowels

landed	ask	glad	milk	smoke
plate	tested	quit	gold	track
hope	swayed	thick	cash	filled
spelled	mink	top	winked	long
crushed	end	stayed	smelled	talk

Did you use tape to shut the box?

She crushed the nut with a rock.

The cat smelled fish.

The plane landed on time.

The kite has a long string.

Can I use that glass?

We live next to the lake.

The old man told a joke and winked at us.

Mom filled my glass to the rim with milk.

Zack yelled when Al pinched him.

-ed, review -ay, exceptions, so, he, fly, V-e, tch, ck, qu, wa, al,
ff, ll, ss, nk, ng, wh, th, ch, sh, short vowels

Decoding/Sentence Reading 2

A Day of Play at Black Cove

It was a hot, hot day. Hal and Eve were at Black Cove. Hal watched Eve play in the sand by a big hole someone had dug. She sifted the sand. Then she filled a bucket to the top and dumped the sand into the hole.

"What's up, Sis?" Hal asked Eve.

"I want to fill up this hole so that no one falls in!" said Eve.

She filled the bucket, dumped it, filled it, dumped it, filled it, and dumped it. This went on and on. Hal watched the small tot. At last the hole was full.

"What can I do next?" asked Eve.

"We can take a walk," said Hal. He brushed Eve off, and they walked on the sand. Eve walked with such small steps. She held Hal's hand, so he did not walk fast.

They talked as they walked. They wanted to find shells. A wave came up fast and sprayed them. Hal splashed Eve, and she splashed him. They both yelled. Then Hal picked

-ed, review -ay, exceptions, *so, he, fly, V-e, tch, ck, qu, wa, al, ff, ll, ss, nk, ng, wh, th, ch, sh,* short vowels

A Day of Play at Black Cove

up a pink shell that had washed up on the shore. He handed it to Eve, and she thanked him. They walked on some more.

At last, Hal said, "Well, we have gone a long way. It is time to go back. Let's get into the shade, Sis. I do not want you to get a lot of sun."

"Why not?" asked Eve.

"Well, there was a man who stayed in the sun a long, long time," said Hal with a grin. "He melted!"

"He did not," yelled Eve. "You just told me a joke."

"Yes, I did," said Hal. "But let's walk back in the shade, just to be on the safe side!"

So Eve held Hal's hand and walked in the shade all the way back.

-ed, review -ay, exceptions, so, he, fly, V-e, tch, ck, qu, wa, al,
ff, ll, ss, nk, ng, wh, th, ch, sh, **short vowels**
A Day of Play at Black Cove

sanded	played	rushed	slope	rose
winked	blame	these	went	hid
rested	blinked	rust	trusted	frog
drip	pinched	drive	tested	hide
lamp	crab	clam	state	quit

Robin rested in bed.

The crab pinched Sal on the leg.

What state do you live in?

Dad winked at Min when she hit the ball.

Mom rushed home to get some more cash.

The lamp was left on all day.

Where has the day gone?

The frog jumped when Bill almost sat on him.

The sun made Fred blink.

Mom sniffed the milk to check if it was bad.

*-ed, review -ay, exceptions, so, he, fly, V-e, tch, ck, qu, wa, al,
ff, ll, ss, nk, ng, wh, th, ch, sh, short vowels*

Decoding/Sentence Reading 3

Time to Hang Up!

Jay felt ill. Mom wanted to go to the store to get something to help him.

"Can you also get some jam?" asked Jay.

"Yes, I can," said Mom. "I will put it on my list. I will be back in a while. You stay in bed!"

Mom went to shop. Jay sat on his bed and played a game. He did not like to be by himself. He wanted to be with his pals. So he called Rick. They talked and talked, then talked some more.

Mom drove to the store. She picked up something to help Jay and went to pay the man. "Where is my list?" she asked herself. "No! I must have left it at home. Well, Jay can tell me what is on it. I will call him."

It was no use. Jay and Rick still talked. Jay had just told Rick a joke. Then Rick told Jay a joke. Mom gave up.

She drove to Dad's shop. They talked as he fixed a lamp. Then Mom called home. It was no use. Jay and Rick still

-ed, review *-ay*, exceptions, *so, he, fly, V-e, tch, ck, qu, wa, al,*
ff, ll, ss, nk, ng, wh, th, ch, sh, short vowels
Time to Hang Up!

43

talked. Rick had just told Jay an old tale. Then Jay told Rick an old tale. Mom gave up.

At last, Jay hung up when Mom got home. "Mom!" he called. "Did you get the jam?"

Mom walked in. "No, I did not," she said. "I left my list at home. I called you and called you, but I did not get through. I wanted you to tell me what was on the list."

"Jam," said Jay. "Jam was on the list. I talked with Rick while you were gone."

"Well, there is no jam today," said Mom. "Next time, do not talk so long!"

-ed, review -ay, exceptions, so, he, fly, V-e, tch, ck, qu, wa, al, ff, ll, ss, nk, ng, wh, th, ch, sh, short vowels

Time to Hang Up!

Suffixes

s	es	ing	er	est	en
pins	lunches	wishing	jumper	fastest	golden
cats	dishes	fishing	boxer	longest	olden
dogs	boxes	lifting	player	pinkest	lengthen
frogs	wishes	sending	colder	wildest	strengthen
lamps	benches	thinking	holder	coldest	thicken

ish	ly	y	ful	ness	less
pinkish	gladly	sandy	playful	kindness	endless
coldish	safely	windy	wishful	gladness	restless
selfish	boldly	rusty	restful	sadness	matchless
smallish	softly	frisky	helpful	boldness	hatless
tallish	bravely	lucky	useful	coldness	hopeless

New Sight Words

goes, does

Review Sight Words

the, has, is, a, his, I, was, to, do, said, what, you, who, into, of, full, pull, push, put, through, your, walk, talk, want, live, give, have, one, done, some, come, something, someone, where, there, were, are, somewhere, love, gone, both, climb, clothes, they, says, today

ditches	melted	grayish	send	chicken
jokes	make	bravely	clap	silken
risking	spend	sniff	bite	nine
let	bat	pipe	hunted	restful
jumper	west	seller	such	blameless

I do not mind you sitting on the bench.

Lin and Jo are jumping rope.

The wild cat gave me a scare.

Frank is sicker today than he was on Sunday.

Jules sold the most cakes at the sale.

I want to help the lost child quickly find his mom.

Did you find my list?

The blind man walked with a cane.

He wore his oldest socks.

Ellen spoke softly.

suffixes, review *-ed, -ay,* **exceptions,** *so, he, fly,*
V-e, tch, ck, qu, wa, al, ff, ll, ss, nk, ng, wh, th, ch, sh, **short vowels**
Decoding/Sentence Reading 1

The Yelling Tot

Mom was in the subway. She was sitting on a bench, holding Ben. He was yelling. Mom wanted to hush the tot. But Ben just kept yelling, and it made Mom blush. She began singing to the tot, but he still yelled. She began to play a game with him, but it was no use. She began to rock him, but he just jumped off her lap. Then he ran to some benches, banged on them, and yelled.

Mom ran and got the tot. She sat him on the bench. Mom began to think. What can I do? She wanted Ben to stop yelling. She picked him up. His pants were dusty. Mom brushed off his pants.

Suddenly, Mom said, "What?" Something had pricked Mom's hand! It was a pin on Ben's pants. She checked his pants to find the pin that had stuck him. Mom yanked the pin off. Then Ben became still and gave Mom a big smile. She and the tot were both glad!

suffixes, review *-ed,-ay*, exceptions, *so, he, fly,*
V-e, tch, ck, qu, wa, al, ff, ll, ss, nk, ng, wh, th, ch, sh, short vowels
The Yelling Tot

sprayed	checked	hope	playmate	hot
yelling	slide	pinch	pinched	wishes
wish	wishing	wished	wishful	when
singing	sings	sing	stop	pants
shed	went	made	just	here

I hope the plane lands on time.

This slide <u>does</u> go fast.

I like the song Mom is singing.

What state do you live in?

That is wishful thinking.

We made it just in time.

I like the song you are singing.

I hope you can come on Sunday.

The skunk sprayed the dog.

The subway ride was fun.

suffixes, review *-ed*, *-ay*, exceptions, *so, he, fly,*
V-e, tch, ck, qu, wa, al, ff, ll, ss, nk, ng, wh, th, ch, sh, short vowels
Decoding/Sentence Reading 2

No Time to Ride

James wants to save a lot of cash. He has some in the bank, but he wants to get some more.

He wants to get a top-grade bike. His old clunky bike has a flat tire and a bent rim that he cannot fix.

James sits and thinks. All of a sudden, he hits upon a plan. He will be a pet watcher, watching a pet when someone <u>goes</u> on a trip. Yes, he will set up a Pet-Watcher Shop! What if he watches more than one pet at a time? That way, he can get more cash and have a useful job.

James sets up his Pet-Watcher Shop. The next day, Kelly brings in her pet dog, Rusty. James is thrilled. Kelly stays while James pets Rusty and talks softly to him. Then she <u>goes</u>. She will pay James when she gets back. The dog misses Kelly, but begins to like James.

suffixes, review *-ed,-ay*, exceptions, *so, he, fly,*
V-e, tch, ck, qu, wa, al, ff, ll, ss, nk, ng, wh, th, ch, sh, short vowels
No Time to Ride

Kelly comes back in six days. She is thankful that she left her dog with James. Rusty is more playful and stronger than before. What a job James has done! Kelly tells all her pals. They want James to watch more pets.

Before long, James has lots of pets to take care of. James also has lots of cash! He <u>goes</u> with his mom to the bike shop and gets the bike he wants.

On the way home, James is singing. "I am so lucky!" he says to his mom. The next thing James has to do is find time to ride his top-grade bike. He <u>does</u> spend so much time at his Pet-Watcher Shop!

suffixes, review *-ed*, *-ay*, exceptions, *so*, *he*, *fly*,
V-e, *tch*, *ck*, *qu*, *wa*, *al*, *ff*, *ll*, *ss*, *nk*, *ng*, *wh*, *th*, *ch*, *sh*, short vowels
No Time to Ride

pets	calling	punched	sadly	talk
lunch	safely	lifeless	much	hitches
pitches	singing	illness	rang	boxes
off	kisses	fastest	stay	lucky
rocky	pack	way	wishing	wished

Seth is the fastest kid in the class.

The bell rang before lunch.

This string is useless.

Jill wished that she had a pet.

Allen is singing a song.

Ted felt bad when he smashed up his bike.

Dale misses his pal.

Jan felt lucky.

<u>Does</u> the sandwich have jam on it?

The man helped Tim cross safely.

suffixes, review *-ed,-ay*, exceptions, *so, he, fly,*
V-e, tch, ck, qu, wa, al, ff, ll, ss, nk, ng, wh, th, ch, sh, short vowels
Decoding/Sentence Reading 3

51

Clams

Pete went to the shore and walked a while on the sand. He had a job to do. Pete wanted to dig up clams, but he did not want to make a mess. He was careful to pick a spot where no one lay on the sand. Then he began to dig.

Pete sang softly to himself. As he dug, he put the sand next to the hole. When he came to a clam, he was careful not to poke the clamshell. He quickly checked all the clams that he had dug up. He wanted to check that the shells were not cracked. It was bad to sell clams with cracked shells.

Pete filled ten small boxes with clams. He did not want to stay longer, so he carefully filled up the holes with sand. Then he brushed off his sandy hands and picked up five boxes. He put the boxes in his truck. Then he got the rest of the boxes and put them in the truck.

Pete was going to take the clams and sell them to The Clam Shack. This was the top spot to go to if you wanted to dine on the best clams, and Pete had the best clams to sell.

suffixes, review *-ed*, *-ay*, exceptions, *so, he, fly,*
V-e, tch, ck, qu, wa, al, ff, ll, ss, nk, ng, wh, th, ch, sh, short vowels

Clams

more	checked	going	flying	quite
crabs	swam	last	may	store
madness	skate	slide	cracking	hatch
chess	stayed	think	boxes	longer
stronger	sadly	playful	itches	bite

That plane is not flying today.

Brad is stronger than I am.

The cat is playful.

Missy stayed late at June's.

I think I want ten boxes.

This jump rope is longer than yours.

He was filled with sadness.

The chick is hatching as the hen watches.

This bug bite itches.

Bob goes home quickly.

suffixes, review *-ed*, *-ay*, exceptions, *so, he, fly,*
V-e, tch, ck, qu, wa, al, ff, ll, ss, nk, ng, wh, th, ch, sh, short vowels
Decoding/Sentence Reading 4

The Camping Trip

It was a fine day to go on a camping trip. All the things were packed in the van. It was full.

"<u>Does</u> all this stuff have to come with us?" asked Dad.

"Yes," said Mom. "There is no store at our camp site. And I must take my plants to water. I have to take care of them."

"If you say so," said Dad. "Climb in, kids."

"No way!" yelled the five kids. "We do not fit in with all this stuff in the van!"

"Some things will have to go," said Dad. "A camping trip is no fun if the kids stay home!"

"Dad! Mom!" said all the kids. "We do not want to stay home! Help us fit in the van!"

"Take all the backpacks, and put them in the case on top of the van," said Dad.

The kids did what Dad said. Then Dan and Fran climbed in. No more kids fit in the van.

suffixes, review *-ed*, *-ay*, exceptions, *so, he, fly,*
V-e, tch, ck, qu, wa, al, ff, ll, ss, nk, ng, wh, th, ch, sh, short vowels
The Camping Trip

"Take my plants and ask Miss Hill to water them," said Mom.

Stan and Jan ran to Miss Hill's. She gladly said yes. Stan and Jan handed the plants to Miss Hill and ran back.

Stan and Jan both climbed into the van. One kid was left.

"Take that big box and put it back in the kitchen," said Mom. "We will take just one pot and one pan."

Nan got in the van. No more kids were left. "Yay!" yelled the five kids.

"Yes!" said Dad. "We are all here!"

"Off we go!" said Mom with a smile. "We are going to have a lot of fun!"

The kids began to play a game in the back of the van.

"This is going to be a restful trip," said Dad as he gave Mom a kiss and a hug. "Sit back and try to take a nap!"

"Thanks. You are a doll," said Mom. She drifted off into a nap.

suffixes, review *-ed,-ay*, exceptions, *so, he, fly,*
V-e, tch, ck, qu, wa, al, ff, ll, ss, nk, ng, wh, th, ch, sh, short vowels
The Camping Trip

55

Twin-Consonant Syllable Division

supper	offer	blubber	ruddy	tennis
scatter	thinner	lesson	dinner	bonnet
traffic	holly	litter	happy	puppy
jelly	belly	penny	daddy	rabbit
mommy	Nelly	muffin	puffin	wallet
happen	sudden	patted	Dennis	kitten
bunny	funny	muddy	napping	sunny

Review Sight Words

the, has, is, a, his, I, was, to, do, said, what, you, who,
into, of, full, pull, push, put, through, your, walk, talk,
want, live, give, have, one, done, some, come, something,
someone, where, there, were, are, somewhere, love, gone,
both, climb, clothes, they, says, today, goes, does

puffin	careful	ditch	pants	puppy
daddy	muffin	ate	wore	happy
happen	hide	get	tricks	stuck
penny	thinner	wish	home	lost
slides	wished	spinning	time	shell

The puffin sat on the rock and ate fish.

I happen to like to play with you.

Daddy ate the muffin that I made.

I am so happy that you came.

The top is spinning.

Be careful not to step on the shells.

The man did a lot of funny tricks.

I wish that spring were here.

Jenny lost a lucky penny on the way home.

The pants had a rip in one leg.

twin-consonant syllable division, review suffixes, *-ed, -ay,* exceptions,   **57**
***so, he, fly, V-e, tch, ck, qu, wa, al, ff, ll, ss, nk, ng, wh, th, ch, sh,* short vowels**
Decoding/Sentence Reading 1

Helpful Pals

Matty is Cal's biggest fan. When he plays baseball, she goes to all his games.

Matty sits in the stands and yells when Cal gets a hit and when he makes a catch. Cal does not mind. He is happy to have such a pal.

Cal does the same thing when Matty plays tennis. He goes to all her games. He is her biggest fan. He sits in the stands and claps when she hits the ball well. He yells when she wins a game, a set, or the match. Matty is happy to have such a pal.

Matty and Cal go to plays if Cal's pal Mike is acting in them. Mike is quite happy when Matty and Cal can come to watch him act.

When Mike does his act, Matty and Cal clap. When he says his lines well, they smile. When the play is done, they stand up and yell. Mike likes his pals to come to all of his plays.

Your pals can be helpful when they are also your fans. Next time your pal does something, offer to go and watch. Be useful and yell when your pal does something well!

twin-consonant syllable division, review suffixes, *-ed*, *-ay*, exceptions,
so, he, fly, V-e, tch, ck, qu, wa, al, ff, ll, ss, nk, ng, wh, th, ch, sh, short vowels

Helpful Pals

butter	hotter	chin	state	store
rubber	stopping	stove	smile	flash
went	thinner	men	man	pitch
misses	madly	longer	struck	sunny
stay	played	checked	packed	choke

The smaller dog ran faster than the big one.

Sam packed his lunch.

The clock struck ten.

Jill stayed and played all day.

Polly played badly.

A sunny day makes me happy.

Mom is stopping on the way home to pick up dinner.

The butter melted in the pan on the stove.

The ball is made of rubber.

The rabbit kept tipping the box on its side.

twin-consonant syllable division, review suffixes, *-ed*, *-ay*, exceptions,
so, he, fly, V-e, tch, ck, qu, wa, al, ff, ll, ss, nk, ng, wh, th, ch, sh, short vowels
Decoding/Sentence Reading 2

59

Mom Helps

Shelly did not want Mom to pack her lunch.

"I do not like this muffin. And I do not like this lunch," said Shelly. "Why do you make it?"

"I want you to stay well," said Mom. "I care, Shelly. I want you to be fit and safe. I love you bunches!"

Shelly did not talk to Mom. She just got up to go.

"It's cold today. Put on your hat and mittens," said Mom.

Shelly got mad. "Mom, I am ten!" she yelled. "I can dress myself!"

Shelly left in a huff. She left her hat and mittens at home. She walked fast. But in a while, she was so cold that she wanted to cry.

Shelly wished that she had not left in such a huff. She wished that she had on her hat and mittens. She felt sad that she had gotten mad at Mom.

60   twin-consonant syllable division, review suffixes, *-ed*, *-ay*, exceptions, *so, he, fly, V-e, tch, ck, qu, wa, al, ff, ll, ss, nk, ng, wh, th, ch, sh,* short vowels

Mom Helps

Just then, Shelly got a big hug. Mom had run all the way to give her the hat and mittens that Shelly had left at home! Mom handed them to Shelly with a wink.

Shelly was so glad that Mom was there! She gave her a hug and kissed her. "I am glad that you watch me," said Shelly. "I am sad that I got mad."

Then Mom went back home, and Shelly went on her way. This time, she was not cold. She felt much better.

twin-consonant syllable division, review suffixes, *-ed*, *-ay*, exceptions,   **61**
so, *he*, *fly*, *V-e*, *tch*, *ck*, *qu*, *wa*, *al*, *ff*, *ll*, *ss*, *nk*, *ng*, *wh*, *th*, *ch*, *sh*, short vowels
Mom Helps

runner	fastest	litter	kittens	traffic
happen	better	mitten	careful	wife
happy	funny	coldest	day	grinning
asking	patches	player	rusty	dinner
hatless	hopping	stopped	butter	bold

Peggy was the fastest runner in the class.

The small child lost a red mitten.

The cat had a litter of kittens.

The man was hatless on the coldest day.

The butter melted on the hot roll.

The rabbit was hopping in the grass.

You had better be careful going home.

When you are funny, it makes me happy.

What happened to you?

The can was rusty.

twin-consonant syllable division, review suffixes, *-ed, -ay*, exceptions,
so, he, fly, V-e, tch, ck, qu, wa, al, ff, ll, ss, nk, ng, wh, th, ch, sh, short vowels

Decoding/Sentence Reading 3

The Traffic Jam

Andy had a long drive home so he was mad when there was a lot of traffic and he got stuck in a jam. Andy badly wanted to get home. He had spent a long day at his job. He wanted his dinner!

"What is the matter with this traffic?" Andy asked himself. "I cannot sit here much longer! I am going to be late. Am I missing dinner? I had better call Beth."

Andy called his wife to tell her that he was going to be late.

"I am happy you called," said Beth. "I will hold dinner. I made fish and chips, Andy. It's what you like best. It will be hot when you get home."

Andy began to think of dinner. In his mind, he smelled the fish. He sat there grinning.

Just then, the traffic began to go. As he sped up, Andy felt glad.

"Fish and chips, here I come!" he yelled.

twin-consonant syllable division, review suffixes, *-ed*, *-ay*, exceptions,

so, *he*, *fly*, *V-e*, *tch*, *ck*, *qu*, *wa*, *al*, *ff*, *ll*, *ss*, *nk*, *ng*, *wh*, *th*, *ch*, *sh*, short vowels

The Traffic Jam

63

rested	drive	wet	called	sled
bitter	shop	walked	humming	happened
tune	plan	muddy	bunny	jogged
rubber	stayed	time	long	went
played	tell	flash	plane	stand

Dad rested while Mom drove.

The bunny rabbit jumped.

May I use the rubber stamp?

Jed stayed a long time at Jim's.

What do you have to say?

Fred played in the muddy water.

Chen was humming a happy tune.

The dog smelled the skunk and ran.

Lilly has to take care of ten pets.

I called you the last time I was here.

twin-consonant syllable division, review suffixes, *-ed*, *-ay*, exceptions,
so, he, fly, V-e, tch, ck, qu, wa, al, ff, ll, ss, nk, ng, wh, th, ch, sh, short vowels

Decoding/Sentence Reading 4

The Best

Abby was the fastest runner in her class.

She had jogged with her mom from the time she was just a small child. But she wanted to run faster than a jog. Running became her hobby. At the age of ten, Abby got a winner's cup. She had run the fastest mile of all the kids in her state.

Then when Abby was 16, she was set to go in the ten mile run. Lots of the best runners in the state were going to run. The winner got a big prize. Abby was thrilled to be a runner. But she also wanted to be the winner.

On the big day, it was hot and windy. Abby felt fit and strong. When the man yelled "Go," Abby set off with the rest of the runners. She was running well.

Abby was running up a hill when it happened. She got a cramp in her left leg. She had to stop, sit on the sidelines, and rub her leg. All the runners ran past Abby. She felt sick. The run was not going well at all!

twin-consonant syllable division, review suffixes, *-ed*, *-ay*, exceptions, *so*, *he*, *fly*, *V-e*, *tch*, *ck*, *qu*, *wa*, *al*, *ff*, *ll*, *ss*, *nk*, *ng*, *wh*, *th*, *ch*, *sh*, short vowels
The Best

Abby got back up to run, but the cramp was still there. Her leg throbbed.

"It's just not your day," someone called to her. "Give up!"

"No," Abby said grimly. "I may not win, but I will not be a quitter."

She got up and began limping her way to the end of the run. She crossed the line last. Her mom and dad ran to her and gave her a big hug.

"Well, I did not win this time," Abby said.

"Yes, you did," said her dad. "You did not quit. That makes you a winner. The best kind of winner!"

Abby nodded. "I did my best," she said softly. "That's all I can do!"

66 twin-consonant syllable division, review suffixes, *-ed*, *-ay*, exceptions, *so, he, fly, V-e, tch, ck, qu, wa, al, ff, ll, ss, nk, ng, wh, th, ch, sh,* short vowels

The Best

Nontwin-Consonant Syllable Division

basket	dentist	tonsil
helmet	risky	unzip
magnet	until	absent
napkin	album	bandit
compact	sapling	picnic
velvet	sunset	contest
selfish	unless	skillet
reptile	canyon	tablet
umpire	plastic	mascot

New Sight Words

danger, strange, listen, wonder

Review Sight Words

the, has, is, a, his, I, was, to, do, said, what, you, who, into, of, full, pull, push, put, through, your, walk, talk, want, live, give, have, one, done, some, come, something, someone, where, there, were, are, somewhere, love, gone, both, climb, clothes, they, says, today, goes, does

napkin	picnic	tinsel	bandit	can
dentist	contest	rabbit	clock	when
umpire	rested	stayed	playing	that
whack	reptile	chess	drink	this
flatten	admire	tossed	bravely	ripe

Sally put the napkin in her lap before dinner.

The umpire called the pitch a strike.

A snake is a reptile.

The tack flattened the tire.

The bandit stole all the gold from the safe.

King Tut had a lot of gold in his grave.

I admire Ken.

The rabbit rested under the steps.

The chess contest lasted a long time.

It was <u>strange</u> that Tim wanted to end the contest before it began.

68 nontwin-consonant syllable division, review twin-consonant syllable division, suffixes, *-ed, -ay,*
exceptions, *so, he, fly, V-e, tch, ck, qu, wa, al, ff, ll, ss, nk, ng, wh, th, ch, sh,* short vowels
Decoding/Sentence Reading 1

A Play

Penny and her pal Pablo were planning to do a skit for the class contest. They wanted the skit to be funny.

Penny dressed up like an old man. She wore an old hat, a red vest, and gray checked pants. She had a picnic basket with a small white bunny rabbit inside.

Pablo dressed up like a bandit. He had on a black mask and a helmet. His bandit was planning to kidnap the bunny that was in Penny's basket.

When the skit began, Penny came into the class from the hall. Pablo walked in behind her. He was humming a tune. Penny just kept walking.

All of a sudden, Pablo grabbed at the basket. The bunny got upset and jumped into Penny's hands! Then the bunny hopped onto Penny's hat. The hat fell off, and the rabbit went hopping into the class.

nontwin-consonant syllable division, review twin-consonant syllable division, suffixes, *-ed*, 69
-ay, exceptions, *so, he, fly, V-e, tch, ck, qu, wa, al, ff, ll, ss, nk, ng, wh, th, ch, sh*, short vowels
A Play

The children in the class yelled as the rabbit hopped past them. Penny and Pablo ran to catch the bunny rabbit, and Pablo fell and lost his helmet. Penny ran into him and fell as well! The rabbit sat still and watched them get up.

Pablo and Penny did not get upset. They had not planned it, but the skit was quite funny this way. So they just kept going. At last, they got the rabbit and the skit ended.

Penny and Pablo's skit was the winner of the contest. It was the most fun to watch. Also, Pablo and Penny kept on acting when things began to go badly.

And the bunny that had made such a mess of the play? It became the class mascot!

70 nontwin-consonant syllable division, review twin-consonant syllable division, suffixes, *-ed, -ay,* exceptions, *so, he, fly, V-e, tch, ck, qu, wa, al, ff, ll, ss, nk, ng, wh, th, ch, sh,* short vowels

A Play

wallet	chick	rubbish	sunfish	nuts
rest	dump	muffin	snapping	stole
madly	longer	longest	trying	check
litter	funny	smelled	letter	complete
plastic	back	packing	trip	grateful

Have you sent a letter to Mel yet?

The cat had a litter of kittens.

Are you packing the plastic plates?

The puffin rested on the rock.

Gil lost his wallet on the hike.

This is the best fishing pole.

Did the trash man take all the rubbish?

What is that <u>strange</u> smell?

Kim has to take care of ten pets.

I ate ten muffins.

nontwin-consonant syllable division, review twin-consonant syllable division, suffixes, *-ed*, **71**
-ay, exceptions, *so, he, fly, V-e, tch, ck, qu, wa, al, ff, ll, ss, nk, ng, wh, th, ch, sh*, short vowels
Decoding/Sentence Reading 2

A Small Bandit

Ellen sat at her desk, holding a letter from her pen pal, Santos, who lived in the West. She had not sent a letter back yet, but she was thinking of doing so today. Ellen missed her old pal.

Ellen got some nuts from the kitchen to snack on and went back to her desk. "I <u>wonder</u> what to say to Santos?" Ellen said as she sat at her desk. "My life is so dull! Nothing has happened that I can tell Santos."

As Ellen got a pen from the desk, some nuts dropped onto the rug. Just then, Ellen felt something brush her sock. As she bent to check, a small furry thing whizzed by and grabbed a nut! Ellen yelled.

Mom came running in. "What is the matter, Ellen? Are you in <u>danger</u>? Is a robber trying to get in?"

"Kind of," Ellen said. "A chipmunk is here inside! It stole some nuts that I dropped."

Just then, Ellen's dog came running in and jumped up

72 nontwin-consonant syllable division, review twin-consonant syllable division, suffixes, *-ed*, *-ay*, exceptions, *so, he, fly, V-e, tch, ck, qu, wa, al, ff, ll, ss, nk, ng, wh, th, ch, sh*, short vowels

A Small Bandit

on the bed. He banged the bed stand and the bedside lamp fell off and broke.

The chipmunk was under the bed when the lamp fell. It came running and jumped past Mom to get to a hole in the wall. The dog yelped and jumped off the bed to try to catch the chipmunk. The dog ran into Mom, who fell back and upset a big shelf. All the things on the shelf went flying.

Dad ran in and stepped on a nut that the chipmunk had dropped. He began to slip and landed on top of Mom. She yelled and pushed him off. Dad sat up and rubbed his leg. At last, it was calm.

"What a mess!" said Ellen. "And one small chipmunk did it all. He made this spot a combat zone! Well, I am grateful to him," said Ellen with a smile. "I have something to say! I can tell Santos all the funny things that just happened. I am so happy!"

"You may think this is funny," said Mom and Dad, "but we think it is a complete mess!"

nontwin-consonant syllable division, review twin-consonant syllable division, suffixes, *-ed*,   73
-ay, exceptions, *so, he, fly, V-e, tch, ck, qu, wa, al, ff, ll, ss, nk, ng, wh, th, ch, sh,* short vowels
A Small Bandit

thinking	missed	under	until	chess
playing	monster	with	rabbit	helmet
choke	cash	children	win	stayed
from	doll	rubber	happened	plastic
clock	bucket	hundred	whiff	matter

Until you play chess with me, I will not be happy.

What happened to that doll?

Do not ride your bike unless you have on your helmet.

May I have a rubber band?

Did you get a whiff of that skunk?

The clock struck ten.

What is the matter with you?

The rabbit hid under the bed.

Kristin was upset and spoke crossly to her pal.

Greg had on a silly pom-pom hat that belonged to his sister.

74 nontwin-consonant syllable division, review twin-consonant syllable division, suffixes, *-ed*, *-ay*, exceptions, *so, he, fly, V-e, tch, ck, qu, wa, al, ff, ll, ss, nk, ng, wh, th, ch, sh,* short vowels

Decoding/Sentence Reading 3

The Snake Pit

It was a cold, crisp fall day. The hunter was just setting off with his dog.

A rabbit watched the sunrise on the hill. He lapped drops of water off the grass. He snipped off a bit of sapling, carefully listening. Suddenly, he smelled the hunter and the dog. Unless he left quickly, he was in <u>danger</u>. He was in <u>danger</u> of ending up in the hunter's skillet the next day!

The rabbit felt the man's steps and smelled the dog.

"I must hide quickly and stay still until they have passed," the rabbit said to himself. "I do not want the dog to smell my tracks." He went into a hole to sit until the hunter and his dog went by.

Suddenly, a small grass snake came up from the bottom of the hole.

"Hiss, hiss. What are you doing here?" said the reptile. "This is my snake pit. Unless you go, I will have to bite you."

nontwin-consonant syllable division, review twin-consonant syllable division, suffixes, *-ed*, **75**
-ay, exceptions, *so, he, fly, V-e, tch, ck, qu, wa, al, ff, ll, ss, nk, ng, wh, th, ch, sh,* short vowels
The Snake Pit

"Do not be so selfish with your snake pit. I am in <u>danger</u> and I must hide!" said the rabbit. "It is safe here. If you let me stay, I will find you a lovely rock to sit on when the sun shines."

"Fine," said the snake. "You are not in <u>danger</u> here. I will not bite you."

The hunter and his dog passed, and the rabbit and the snake left the snake pit. The rabbit led the snake to a flat rock to sit on in the sunshine.

"This is a fine sunning spot," said the snake. "Thank you!"

"Do not take a long nap in the sun," the rabbit said with a smile. "You must not be here when the hunter and his dog come back!"

76   nontwin-consonant syllable division, review twin-consonant syllable division, suffixes, *-ed*, *-ay*, exceptions, *so, he, fly, V-e, tch, ck, qu, wa, al, ff, ll, ss, nk, ng, wh, th, ch, sh*, short vowels

The Snake Pit

matches	filling	glasses	picnic	temper
rubber	robber	funny	dentist	missing
sock	gave	maze	sandy	supper
until	useful	sniffed	kitchen	penny
lucky	admit	napkin	wallet	selfish

Mom lost her sunglasses in the grass.

The clam digger filled her bucket with clams.

Santos lost his lucky penny.

The dog sniffed to find his bone.

I admit I was late.

What <u>strange</u> shape did you make with your clay?

This basket will be useful.

It is not kind to be selfish.

The man left his wallet at home.

Dad lit the fire with the kitchen matches.

nontwin-consonant syllable division, review twin-consonant syllable division, suffixes, *-ed*,   **77**
-ay, exceptions, *so, he, fly, V-e, tch, ck, qu, wa, al, ff, ll, ss, nk, ng, wh, th, ch, sh*, short vowels
Decoding/Sentence Reading 4

The Humpback Whale

You are a mammal. So are dogs, cats, foxes, and rabbits. And so are whales. Did you think whales were fish? No, they are mammals, but they are mammals that can swim like fish under water!

In many ways, whales are not like fish. They do not have scales like fish. They have soft skin, just like us. Whales also have a thick layer of fat under this skin. It is called blubber. With all that blubber, whales do not get cold.

One kind of whale is called the humpback whale. It is as long as a bus and has a set of long flippers. It also has a small fin on its back. When the whale goes to dive, the fin gives its back a humped shape. This is why this whale is called a humpback.

Yes, the humpback has a fin with a shape like a hump. It also has lots of bumps and lumps on its skin. It may not be a lovely mammal, but it is lovely to watch as it jumps and dives and playfully splashes.

78   nontwin-consonant syllable division, review twin-consonant syllable division, suffixes, *-ed,*
-ay, exceptions, *so, he, fly,* V-e, *tch, ck, qu, wa, al, ff, ll, ss, nk, ng, wh, th, ch, sh,* short vowels
The Humpback Whale

A humpback lives on fish and on small shrimp called krill. One whale has to take in lots and lots and lots of krill at dinnertime!

If you dive, you can swim beside these wonderful whales. A humpback will be quite careful with you. You will not be in <u>danger</u>. The whale is not careless with its long flippers. You will be grateful that these big mammals act with such kindness.

Humpback whales can also sing! They sing quite lovely songs. This may be the way they talk. Those who have listened to the humpback's songs are filled with <u>wonder</u>. If you are lucky, a humpback whale will sing to you!

Humpback whales are endangered. They are almost extinct. There are approximately 20,000 left. Find what can be done to save the humpback whales before they are gone.

nontwin-consonant syllable division, review twin-consonant syllable division, suffixes, *-ed,*   79
-ay, **exceptions,** *so, he, fly, V-e, tch, ck, qu, wa, al, ff, ll, ss, nk, ng, wh, th, ch, sh,* short vowels
The Humpback Whale

ou (mound)

out	our	house	round
found	ouch	couch	pouch
loud	south	mouth	pout
proud	scout	flour	spout
trout	shout	mound	pound
bound	sound	count	mount
hound	ground	wound	sour
slouch	cloud	scour	mouse
blouse		grouse	sprout
stout			

ou (doughnut)

four	course	court
pour	shoulder	fourth
court	dough	mourned
gourd	although	boulder
soul	though	

_ou_ (cousin)

young

tough

touch

country

cousin

slough

rough

enough

_ou_ (you)

you   wound

your   through

group   croup

soup   troupe

New Sight Words

could, would, should

Review Sight Words

the, has, is, a, his, I, was, to, do, said, what, you, who, into, of, full, pull, push, put, through, your, walk, talk, want, live, give, have, one, done, some, come, something, someone, where, there, were, are, somewhere, love, gone, both, climb, clothes, they, says, today, goes, does, strange, danger, listen, wonder

out	rabbit	home	group	runner
basket	coupon	round	happen	testing
black	ground	picnic	count	slipper
kitten	sound	found	shut	invite
four	step	touch	went	tramp

Jake was proud to belong to the scouting group.

I found this ring on the playground.

Do not touch the things on the teacher's desk.

Can you count to a hundred?

What is that loud sound?

Can you come to my house to have dinner?

Jill spilled the flour on the counter.

The kitten slept in the basket.

The batter struck out in the fourth inning.

The top spun round and round.

ou, nontwin-consonant syllable division, review twin-consonant syllable division, suffixes, *-ed*, *ay*, exceptions, *so, he, fly*, vowel-consonant-e, *tch, ck, qu, wa, al, ff, ll, ss, sh, ch, th, wh, ng, nk*, short vowels

Decoding/Sentence Reading 1

The Lost Ring

Kristin found a silver ring in the sand at South Cove. The silver was twisted around in a lovely way. Kristin wanted to find out who it belonged to, so she made a poster. She hung her poster up on the bathhouse wall. The poster said, "Found: One Ring. Call 555-7600 if it is yours."

That same day, Kristin got ten calls about the ring. The callers would say that the ring belonged to them. Kristin would ask them to tell her what the ring was like. Not one of the callers spoke of the twisted silver. So Kristin kept the ring.

She put it inside a big plastic box and pushed the box under the couch in the den.

Lots of time went by, and Kristin did not think much about the ring. Summer passed into fall, and fall passed into winter. At last, spring came back.

One day in May, Kristin and her pal, Lin, went to South Cove. They walked to the spot where Kristin had found the

ou, nontwin-consonant syllable division, review twin-consonant syllable division, suffixes, *-ed, ay,*   83
exceptions, *so, he, fly,* vowel-consonant-e, *tch, ck, qu, wa, al, ff, ll, ss, sh, ch, th, wh, ng, nk,* short vowels
The Lost Ring

ring. They both kicked at the sand. Kristin felt something. She pulled a wallet out of the sand.

When Kristin got home, she gave the wallet to her dad. The wallet was wet and soggy. Dad called the number that he found inside. He spoke to a man called Chen Hong. This was the same name that Dad had found in the wallet.

Chen Hong was so happy to find out that his wallet was found. "It would just make my day if you also found my wife's wedding ring," he said.

With a smile, Dad put Kristin on the line. "Can you tell me about your wife's ring?" she asked.

"It's a lovely ring," said Chen Hong. "The silver is twisted."

"That's the ring I found!" Kristin almost shouted.

"I am so glad!" said the man. "We will be back at South Cove this June. We will get the ring and the wallet then. My wife and I are both thrilled. Thank you so much!"

Kristin felt proud that she had made them so happy.

84 *ou*, nontwin-consonant syllable division, review twin-consonant syllable division, suffixes, *-ed, ay,* exceptions, *so, he, fly,* vowel-consonant-e, *tch, ck, qu, wa, al, ff, ll, ss, sh, ch, th, wh, ng, nk,* short vowels

The Lost Ring

a- (alike)

along

alike

alive

above

away

awhile

across

awake

ago

around

about

amount

around	playing	shouted	costume	stayed
house	stayed	sadly	touch	thankful
rabbit	about	trick	get	state
shout	happen	across	dripping	flying
counting	hundred	sound	mouth	swam

Mom made my costume long ago.

My sister can count to four hundred.

The frog jumped out of my pocket.

Bring along a lunch.

I happen to like to go to the dentist.

I think we should put the couch here.

I will mix the flour into the cake batter.

Calvin was sad while you were away.

The round ball rolled into the tall grass.

I kept popping gumdrops into my mouth.

86 *a-, ou*, nontwin-consonant syllable division, review twin-consonant syllable division, suffixes, *-ed, ay*, exceptions, *so, he, fly*, vowel-consonant-e, *tch, ck, qu, wa, al, ff, ll, ss, sh, ch, th, wh, ng, nk*, short vowels

Decoding/Sentence Reading 2

The Tale of Melvin the Mouse

An old man had a big house filled with pets. There were cats, dogs, pigs, frogs, rabbits, chipmunks, and one mouse. Sometimes, all the pets talked at the same time. It would get so loud that the old man could not think.

When this happened, he would run around to talk to all the pets, one by one. "Hush," he would say softly. "Stay still." And one pet would close its mouth. Then the next one. And the next one. At last, they <u>would</u> all be still.

One day, the old man was going around and hushing up his pets. He got to the spot where the last pet <u>should</u> be, a white mouse called Melvin. But the mouse was not there.

"Where is Melvin?" the old man softly asked a chipmunk called Chip. Chip asked a dog named Duke. In awhile, all the pets were talking quite loudly, wondering where Melvin was.

a-, ou, nontwin-consonant syllable division, review twin-consonant syllable division, suffixes, *-ed*,   **87**
ay, exceptions, *so, he, fly*, vowel-consonant-e, *tch, ck, qu, wa, al, ff, ll, ss, sh, ch, th, wh, ng, nk*, short vowels
The Tale of Melvin the Mouse

While all this was happening, Melvin was outside. He was having a ball. He lay stretched out on the grass, sniffing a rose, and watching the clouds go by. "This is the life," he said to himself. "I love it outside! I hate it inside! I am staying outside."

All of a sudden, a jay rushed from a branch, made a dive, and began to peck at Melvin.

"No! Ouch!" yelled Melvin. He ran and hid behind a rock until the jay left. "That was a close one," he said softly.

"Yes-s-s-s-s, that was close," hissed something behind him.

With a yelp, Melvin spun around. A big black snake lay there, grinning. "My, my," she said to the mouse. "You are so fine and plump. You are the plumpest mouse I have found."

Melvin yelled and dashed out from behind the rock. He skidded to a stop. There in his path crouched a red fox, licking its lips! Melvin gasped, rolled himself into a small ball, and began to shake.

88 *a-, ou*, nontwin-consonant syllable division, review twin-consonant syllable division, suffixes, *-ed, ay*, exceptions, *so, he, fly*, vowel-consonant-*e, tch, ck, qu, wa, al, ff, ll, ss, sh, ch, th, wh, ng, nk*, short vowels

The Tale of Melvin the Mouse

Just then, the old man and all the house pets ran outside. They were all yelling, "Melvin!" The fox spun around and quickly ran off. The house pets helped Melvin walk safely back to the house. And all the way home, Melvin said the same thing: "I love it inside. I hate it outside!"

a-, *ou*, nontwin-consonant syllable division, review twin-consonant syllable division, suffixes, *-ed*,   89
ay, exceptions, *so, he, fly*, vowel-consonant-*e*, *tch, ck, qu, wa, al, ff, ll, ss, sh, ch, th, wh, ng, nk,* short vowels
The Tale of Melvin the Mouse

ground	skillet	pouch	rabbit	trumpet
plenty	tray	cloudy	shed	tryouts
stone	louder	smile	patched	stayed
blouse	wore	winter	slippers	trunk
suddenly	around	funny	away	slim

Plants sprout out of the ground in spring.

We will go south next winter.

Len can shout louder than you.

I put on my bathrobe and slippers when I got out of the bathtub.

I <u>could</u> play with dolls all day.

It was a gray and cloudy day.

Suddenly, Lane walked out of the house.

Did you have enough soup?

I just patched the hole in the wall.

I think Roz is funny.

90 *a-, ou,* nontwin-consonant syllable division, review twin-consonant syllable division, suffixes, *-ed,*
ay, exceptions, *so, he, fly,* vowel-consonant-*e, tch, ck, qu, wa, al, ff, ll, ss, sh, ch, th, wh, ng, nk,* short vowels
Decoding/Sentence Reading 3

A Big Problem

Trish wanted badly to play baseball, but her mom wanted her to play the trumpet. This was a big problem. The trumpet lessons were at the same time as the baseball tryouts and all the baseball games. Trish could not do both. She felt bad. She wanted to do things that made her mother happy. But she did *not* want to play the trumpet.

Trish sat on the steps of her house, sadly watching the clouds go by. Her best pal Brandon stopped by on his way home. He could tell that Trish was sad. She would not smile at his jokes, and those jokes were funny.

She pouted when he asked her what the problem was.

"I just wish I did not have to play the trumpet," Trish said glumly. "I wish Mom would not make me take lessons. I want to be a baseball catcher. I am one of the best catchers around. But I do not play the trumpet well. In fact, I stink!"

a-, ou, nontwin-consonant syllable division, review twin-consonant syllable division, suffixes, *-ed,*   **91**
ay, exceptions, *so, he, fly*, vowel-consonant-*e, tch, ck, qu, wa, al, ff, ll, ss, sh, ch, th, wh, ng, nk*, short vowels
A Big Problem

"Did you try talking to your mom?" asked Brandon.

"No. And I do not want to," Trish told her pal. "Here's the thing. She wanted to play the trumpet when she was small, but her mom did not have the cash. She thinks playing the trumpet is the best thing. It may be best to her, but not to me. Baseball is my best thing."

"I still think you should talk to her," said Brandon. "You have to try!"

"Well, yes," Trish had to admit. "I suppose so." She gave Brandon a hopeful smile.

"That's the way!" Brandon said with a grin. "Hang in there! And tell me what happens."

The next day, Trish woke up at six. She began to think about what she would say. She sat around until her mom woke up. Mom was still in her bathrobe and slippers when Trish went to talk to her.

"Something is on your mind, Trish," Mom said. "I can tell. What is it?"

92 *a-, ou,* nontwin-consonant syllable division, review twin-consonant syllable division, suffixes, *-ed, ay,* exceptions, *so, he, fly,* vowel-consonant-e, *tch, ck, qu, wa, al, ff, ll, ss, sh, ch, th, wh, ng, nk,* short vowels

A Big Problem

"Well, it's this," said Trish. " I do not like to play the trumpet, Mom. What I most want to do is to play baseball. I want to be a catcher. I want to try out today, but I can't."

"Why can't you try out?" asked Mom.

"My trumpet lesson is the same time as the tryouts," Trish said sadly. "And all the baseball games are at the same time as my trumpet lessons."

"Well, that is a problem," said Mom. "Did you just say that you do not like to play the trumpet?"

"Yes," said Trish. "You like it. That is why I play. But I sound bad when I play. It is just no fun at all."

"I think you play fine, Trish," said Mom. "But if you do not like it, it will be difficult to do well. I want you to do something that brings out the best in you. If I did not let you try to be a catcher, you would be sad, the way I was when I <u>could</u> not play the trumpet. So go to the baseball tryout today. Go and do your best."

a-, ou, **nontwin-consonant syllable division, review twin-consonant syllable division, suffixes,** *-ed,*   93
ay, **exceptions,** *so, he, fly,* **vowel-consonant-e,** *tch, ck, qu, wa, al, ff, ll, ss, sh, ch, th, wh, ng, nk,* **short vowels**
A Big Problem

"Mom, I love you!" Trish shouted and gave her mom a hug. "Maybe next fall I will go back to the trumpet, but today I just want to go catch some baseballs!"

Trish left to tell Brandon and to thank him for helping her. On the way, she could not help thinking about her mom. It made her smile.

"I am so glad that I talked to her!" Trish said to herself. She felt proud. "I did a brave thing. And Mom does not expect me to be like her. She just wants me to be the best that I can be!"

It pays to talk things out.

94 *a-*, *ou*, nontwin-consonant syllable division, review twin-consonant syllable division, suffixes, *-ed*, *ay*, exceptions, *so*, *he*, *fly*, vowel-consonant-*e*, *tch*, *ck*, *qu*, *wa*, *al*, *ff*, *ll*, *ss*, *sh*, *ch*, *th*, *wh*, *ng*, *nk*, short vowels

A Big Problem